A QUIZ

Compiled by Julia Skinner

THE FRANCIS FRITH COLLECTION

www.francisfrith.com

First published in the United Kingdom in 2010 by The Francis Frith Collection®

This edition published exclusively for Identity Books in 2010 ISBN 978-1-84589-539-6

British Library Cataloguing in Publication Data

Ask Me Another! Lincolnshire - A Quiz
Compiled by Julia Skinner

The Francis Frith Collection
Frith's Barn, Teffont,
Salisbury, Wiltshire SP3 5QP
Tel: +44 (0) 1722 716 376
Email: info@francisfrith.co.uk
www.francisfrith.com

Printed and bound in Malaysia

Front Cover: **MABLETHORPE, DONKEY RIDES c1955** M1053p

The colour-tinting is for illustrative purposes only, and is not intended to be historically accurate

AS WITH ANY HISTORICAL DATABASE, THE FRANCIS FRITH ARCHIVE IS CONSTANTLY BEING CORRECTED AND IMPROVED, AND THE PUBLISHERS WOULD WELCOME INFORMATION ON OMISSIONS OR INACCURACIES

CONTENTS

QUESTIONS

ANSWERS

QUESTIONS

LINCOLNSHIRE DIALECT WORDS AND PHRASES

1. What does it mean if you 'chunter'?
2. What are 'frim folk'?
3. What is a 'gimmer'?
4. What does it mean if you 'jiffle'?
5. What is 'kelch'?
6. What does 'proggle' mean?
7. What does 'reasty' mean?
8. What is a 'starnil'?
9. If you described someone as being 'uneppen', what would you mean?
10. If you described someone as a 'wassack' or a 'gump', what would you mean?
11. What is a 'yucker'?

MABLETHORPE, MAIN STREET 1890 26717

MABLETHORPE, DONKEY RIDES c1955 M1053

SPORT

12. Annual horse racing events in Lincoln began in 1680 and continued on Lincoln Heath until 1773, after which they were relocated to the West Commons. The most celebrated race was the Lincolnshire Handicap, first run in 1849; the Lincoln races came to an end in 1964 but the 'Lincoln Handicap', as it is now known, still takes place each spring, although it has been transferred to … which other racecourse?

13. Lincoln City FC are nicknamed 'the Imps', but do you know the nickname of their female counterparts, Lincoln City LFC?

14. What is the nickname of Grimsby Town FC?

15. Boston Rowing Club hosts a long-distance rowing race each year whose length of 49 kilometres (31 miles) makes it unique in Britain. What is it called?

16. What is the nickname of Grantham Town Football Club?

17. Which former manager of the England football team once played for Grimsby Town?

18. There are a number of excellent golf courses and golf links in the Skegness area – but do you know what the difference is between a golf course and a golf links?

19. One of English football's most famous goalkeepers was born in Skegness in 1948 and played for Scunthorpe United early in his career – who was he?

ARTS AND LITERATURE

20. A famous composer completed his 'Cotswold Symphony' in Skegness in 1900, whilst he was in the resort playing his trombone in the pier orchestra. Who was he?

21. Whose most famous poetical work is 'High Tide on the Coast of Lincolnshire'?

22. What is the link between Stamford and the fictional detective Inspector Morse?

23. Here's one for Radio 4 listeners: What is the link between the phrase 'without repetition, hesitation or deviation' and Grantham?

24. A statue to a Lincolnshire man who became of England's greatest poets stands in Lincoln – who was he, and where can you find it?

25. Which royal mistress and ancestress of the present royal family is buried in Lincoln Cathedral, and which famous historical novel was written about her?

SKEGNESS, THE PIER
1904 51763

FOLKLORE AND CUSTOMS

26. According to Lincolnshire folklore, what does it mean if a baby is born with exceptionally large ears?

27. What was it customary to do on 'Mumping Day' in Lincolnshire in the past?

28. What in Boston is known as 'the breath of the Devil'?

29. Which riotous ancient custom used to take place through the streets of Stamford in November in past times?

30. One of the stories about the Angel and Royal Hotel at Grantham concerns Michael Soloman, a one-time landlord, who died in 1706. In his will he left 40 shillings to be paid each Michaelmas Day for an unusual purpose which still takes place today – what is this?

31. Can you name the boy being carried on the shoulders of Grim the fisherman on the statue in the grounds of Grimsby College of Technology? (Seen in photograph G60703, opposite.)

GRIMSBY, THE STATUE OF GRIM AT NUNS CORNER 2004 G60703

GRANTHAM, THE ANGEL AND ROYAL HOTEL 1893 33257

HISTORY AND ARCHAEOLOGY

32. The Angel and Royal Hotel in Grantham is one of the oldest inns in England. The façade of the present-day building is of the mid 15th century, but the cellars could be even earlier. A king famously signed a death warrant here whilst staying at the inn (then known as just 'the Angel Inn') during the late Middle Ages – which king, and whose death warrant?

33. Grantham and Stamford in Lincolnshire used to be numbered amongst only twelve towns in England to have something called an Eleanor Cross. What was this?

34. Which of Henry VIII's six wives once lived at the Old Hall at Gainsborough (photograph G145001, below), a 15th-century timber-framed manor house with the most complete medieval kitchen in the country?

35. When did the 'Lincolnshire Rising' take place, and what was it about?

36. Lincolnshire has the oldest canal in England – where is it?

GAINSBOROUGH, THE OLD HALL c1955 G145001

37. Who is the Lucy Tower of Lincoln Castle named after?

38. Like most places in Lincolnshire, Grantham was founded by the Anglo-Saxons, but later came under Danish law when it was included in the 'Danelaw', the part of England that came under Danish rule in the ninth century. There are still many reminders of Grantham's Danish heritage in some of the town's street name endings, such as Swinegate, Watergate and Westgate – but what does the 'gate' part of these names actually mean?

LINCOLN, THE CASTLE 1890 25669

LINCOLN, AERIAL VIEW FROM SOUTH WEST c1960 L49088

39. The great Gothic edifice of Lincoln Cathedral is one of the most impressive cathedrals in Europe. A statue of 'The Swineherd of Stow' can be seen on the pinnacle of the left-hand tower of its west front – who was he, and why is he commemorated like this?

40. Lincolnshire possesses many Anglo-Saxon church towers – usually only the tower of the church was built in stone, as somewhere for local people to take refuge from Viking raids, whilst the rest of the church was wood – and one of England's best examples can be found in the county. Where is it?

STAMFORD, RED LION SQUARE 1922 72300

41. One of the oldest houses in England can be found in Lincoln, now used as the headquarters of the Society for Lincolnshire History and Archaeology. Where is it, and what is it called?

42. How did Red Lion Square in Stamford get its name?

43. How did Cleethorpes Pier come to be part of Leicester City Football Club's ground?

44. The fashion for sea bathing began to catch on in Lincolnshire around the turn of the 18th and 19th centuries, mainly amongst the wealthier classes, and Lincolnshire squires and their families drove to Skegness, Mablethorpe and Freiston Shore to keep in the swing. However, it was only when the railway arrived in 1873 that Skegness really took off as a resort for everyone, mainly as a result of the town being developed by the local landowner – who was he?

45. What is the link between Boston and the 'Mayflower', the ship that carried the Pilgrim Fathers to the USA in 1620?

CLEETHORPES, THE PIER 1906 55741

SKEGNESS, LUMLEY ROAD 1899 44354

46. What is the link between Boston in Lincolnshire and Boston in the USA?

47. Lincolnshire's long coastline is washed by the North Sea – by what name was the North Sea formerly known?

48. How did Union Street and Union Place in Boston get their names?

49. Why did cyclists have to be especially careful when riding on the Great North Road near Stamford in the late 19th century?

50. Where will you find the Lincoln Imp, and what is it?

51. What was the original purpose of the Grimsby Dock Tower, seen in photograph 26722, below?

52. Which famous raid of the Second World War was launched from RAF Scampton near Grantham in 1943?

GRIMSBY, ROYAL DOCK AND THE DOCK TOWER 1890 26722

TRADE AND INDUSTRY

53. It is often said that the tower of the parish church of St Botolph in Boston is 'built on wool'. What does this mean?

54. Medieval Lincoln produced a fine range of cloths; its best and most expensive was known as scarlet, but there was also blanket, which was white, and two varieties known as 'say'; grey and green. Who famously wore clothes made of 'Lincoln green' cloth?

55. Which famous engineering works was formerly associated with Grantham?

56. Which animals kept on the Lincolnshire fens around Boston were referred to as 'the fenman's treasurer' in the past?

57. A famous name in Lincoln's industrial heritage is that of Clayton & Shuttleworth. What was this company particularly famous for making?

58. The armoured fighting vehicle known as the tank was invented and produced in Lincolnshire during the First World War, at the New Wellington Works of Wm Foster Ltd on New Boultham Road in Lincoln. But why were these vehicles called 'tanks'?

GRIMSBY, FISH PONTOON 1906
55749

GENERAL KNOWLEDGE -LINCOLNSHIRE

59. What is the name for someone born and bred in Lincolnshire?

60. What local landmark is affectionately known as 'the Boston Stump'?

61. Why is the dual-carriageway known as John Adams Way in Boston so-named?

62. What is the distinguishing flavour of Lincolnshire sausages?

63. Which wild plant that grows along the Lincolnshire coast is also known as 'poor man's asparagus'?

64. Which Lincolnshire town became the village of 'Meryton' in the 2005 film version of 'Pride and Prejudice', starring Keira Knightley?

65. Why were local people in Scunthorpe feeling 'all shook up' in February 2008?

SCUNTHORPE, HIGH STREET 1904 52160v

STAMFORD, THE STAMFORD HOTEL 1922 72316

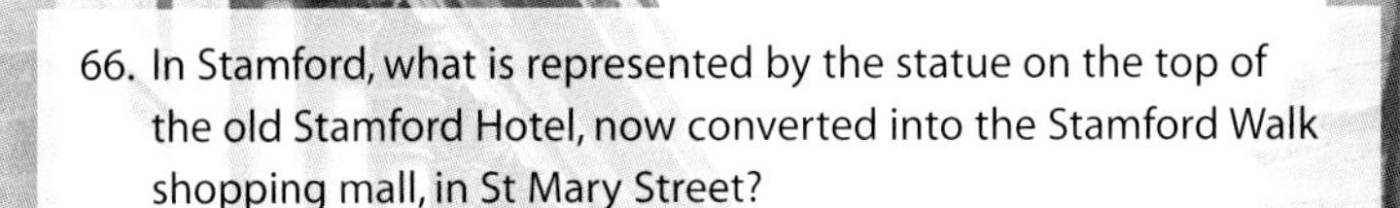

66. In Stamford, what is represented by the statue on the top of the old Stamford Hotel, now converted into the Stamford Walk shopping mall, in St Mary Street?

67. A bronze statue by Ron Walker of a much-loved character who was used on a famous railway poster to publicise Skegness stands on the seafront of the resort, unveiled in 1989 – how is he popularly known?

68. An unusual library can be found in Grantham. What and where is it?

69. Which international festival is held on Cleethorpes Beach each year?

70. How is it now possible to visit an old Stamford shop in the city of York?

71. A Lincolnshire church was praised by Simon Jenkins in 'England's Thousand Best Churches' as having 'the finest steeple in England'. Which church, and in which town?

72. Pisa in Italy is famous for its Leaning Tower – but Lincolnshire has one too! Where is it?

73. Louth was a prosperous, compact market town serving a large area of the central Wolds in the Middle Ages. Its revival in the late 18th and early 19th centuries resulted in some fine town building and re-fronting of earlier buildings. The town is particularly famous for which superb building?

74. A road in Grantham is named Edith Smith Way – who was Edith Smith?

LOUTH, VIEW FROM THE WOLDS c1955 L305014

LINCOLN, STONEBOW 1923 74634

75. The church at Great Ponton near Grantham bears an unusual weather-vane in the shape of … what?

76. What is the origin of the name of Lincoln?

STAMFORD, GEORGE HOTEL 1922 72305

77. Much of 18th-century Stamford's trade came from its location on the Great North Road (now the A1), and it had numerous coaching inns such as the George Hotel, once classed as the best hotel on the Great North Road. Photograph 72305 (above), taken in the 1920s, shows the George Hotel and its unusual sign, which is still there. What is the name for this type of sign?

78. An unusual sight to be seen in Grantham is a 'living sign' for a local pub – what and where is this?

79. Why was Grimsby nicknamed 'Winsby' in the early years of the 21st century?

FAMOUS PEOPLE

80. One of the most famous men in the field of science and mathematics was born in 1643 at Woolsthorpe Manor in Woolsthorpe-by-Colsterworth in Lincolnshire, and went to school in Grantham at the grammar school in the town (the building now known as the Old School and used as a library by King's School) – who was he?

81. Many Lincolnshire men were involved in the exploration of Australia, and the stretch of water between Tasmania and south Australia is named after one of them – what is its name, and who was he?

GRANTHAM, THE OLD GRAMMAR SCHOOL 1890 27850

SPILSBY, FRANKLIN MONUMENT 1956 S391007

82. Dominating the Market Place of Spilsby is a bronze statue of Sir John Franklin, the Arctic explorer who was born in the town in 1786 (see photograph S391007, opposite). He died during his last expedition, trying to find... what?

83. A famous Anglo-Saxon freedom fighter who fought against the Norman invaders of the 11th century was a Lincolnshire man – who was he?

84. The new graveyard of St Martin's Church in Stamford, off Barnack Road, is the final resting place of Daniel Lambert – why was he famous at the time of his death in 1809?

85. How can George Boole, born in Lincoln in 1815, be said to be a pioneer of the modern computer age?

86. Grantham was the birthplace of which famous British politician?

ANSWERS

LINCOLNSHIRE DIALECT WORDS AND PHRASES

1. 'Chunter' means to complain.

2. 'Frim folk' are people from another area.

3. A 'gimmer' is a ewe (a female sheep) which has never given birth.

4. 'Jiffle' means fidgeting.

5. 'Kelch' is mud.

6. 'Proggle' means to poke about, as with a stick.

7. 'Reasty' means rancid, or gone off.

8. A 'starnil' is a starling.

9. 'Uneppen' means clumsy.

10. A 'wassack' or a 'gump' means a fool, or a simpleton.

11. A 'yucker' is a young person.

SPALDING, IN THE BULB FIELDS c1955 S388193

LOUTH, THE CHURCH FROM EASTGATE c1955 L305016

SPORT

12. The 'Lincoln Handicap' race now takes place at Doncaster racecourse in South Yorkshire, where it remains central to the flat-racing calendar, being the opening race of the season.

13. 'The Lady Imps'.

14. 'The Mariners'.

15. The Boston Rowing Marathon. The course of the race is along the River Witham from Lincoln to Boston, starting at Brayford Pool in Lincoln and finishing at the Boston clubhouse.

16. Grantham Town Football Club is nicknamed 'The Gingerbreads' after the Grantham Gingerbread that the town is famous for.

17. Former England national football team manager Graham Taylor was once the fullback for Grimsby Town.

18. To classify as a links, a golf course must be within sight of the sea.

19. Raymond, or 'Ray', Clemence, born in the town in 1948, who played for Scunthorpe United, Liverpool, Tottenham Hotspur and was capped 61 times for England. He is considered to have been one of England's best-ever goalkeepers.

LINCOLN, THE TENNYSON STATUE 1906 55109

ARTS AND LITERATURE

20. Gustav Holst. It is recorded that 'he scored his Cotswold Symphony in his free time on the sands' whilst he was living and working in the town.

21. Jean Ingelow (1820-97), who was born in South Square in Boston. She became a successful poet who was admired in Britain as well as in the United States.

22. The writer Colin Dexter, creator of the popular Inspector Morse books, was born in Stamford in 1930 and educated at Stamford School, the boys' public school in the town which was founded in 1532. Inspector Morse himself was described in the novels as an 'Old Stamfordian'.

23. Nicholas Parsons, presenter of the BBC Radio 4 comedy panel game 'Just a Minute', when panellists have to talk for one minute on a given subject 'without repetition, hesitation or deviation'. He was born in Grantham in 1923, the son of a local doctor.

24. Just outside the cathedral close in Lincoln is a statue of Alfred, Lord Tennyson, who was born in Somersby on the Wolds in 1809 (see photograph 55109, opposite). The bronze statue shows Tennyson deep in thought, accompanied by his Siberian wolfhound, Karenina.

25. Katherine (or Catherine) Swynford, the mistress of John of Gaunt (one of the sons of Edward III), and mother to four of his children; the couple eventually married. One of the children was John Beaufort, from whom all of England's succeeding royal families can be traced. She died in 1405, and her story inspired Anya Seton's famous historical novel 'Katherine'.

FOLKLORE AND CUSTOMS

26. It was an old Lincolnshire belief that when a baby was born with noticeably large ears, it was a sign that he or she would be successful in life.

27. On 'Mumping Day' – St Thomas's Day, 21st December – it was the custom in Lincolnshire for poor people to go around begging for Christmas fare.

28. The tower of St Botolph's Church in Boston is the tallest parish church tower (exclusive of spire) in England, and local folklore says the strong winds that blow around the tower, known as the 'breath of the Devil', are the result of a struggle for power that once took place between St Botolph and the Devil. Apparently, St Botulph preached at the Devil so fervently that he was left speechless, and could only huff and puff helplessly as he sought for words to argue back.

29. November used to be the time when the custom of bull running, or 'rebel's riot feast', took place in Stamford. This involved tormenting and chasing an unfortunate beast through the streets of the town, before it was slaughtered for the evening feast. The custom was eventually banned in 1839, due as much to the prohibitive cost of policing as to any enlightened attitude towards animal rights.

30. Michael Soloman left 40 shillings in his will to be paid each Michaelmas Day (29th September) for the preaching of a sermon against drunkenness – this custom endures to this day.

31. Havelok. 'The Lay of Havelok the Dane' tells how Havelok, the orphaned son of the King of Denmark, was cast adrift on the sea by his evil guardian. A raft bore the child to the coast of Lincolnshire where he was found by Grim, the legendary founder of Grimsby, who brought him up as his own son. When he grew up Havelok discovered the truth about his birth and returned to his homeland, eventually becoming King of Denmark. During his youth Havelok became renowned for his feats of strength. He once went to the court of Alsi, the King of Lindsey, at Lincoln, where he worked in the royal kitchens. King Alsi had promised his daughter Goldburga to the strongest and fairest man in the land. At a stone-throwing contest Havelok managed to lift one great stone higher and hurl it further than anyone else, and thus he won the hand of his wife. The Havelok Stone sits outside the Welholme Gallery in Grimsby, though whether this is the very stone reputedly thrown by Havelok to win the hand of Goldburga is for romantics to believe!

HISTORY AND ARCHAEOLOGY

32. It was in the grand upper room of the inn known as the Chambre du Roi, or the King's Room, that in 1483 Richard III heard of the treachery of the Duke of Buckingham and signed his death warrant.

33. In 1290 Queen Eleanor, the beloved wife of King Edward I, died near Lincoln. Her body was taken to London for burial, and King Edward arranged for 12 beautifully decorated stone crosses to be erected on the places along the route where the funeral cortège had stopped for the night. Two of these places were Grantham and Stamford, both of which lost their Eleanor Crosses during the Civil War of the 17th century, destroyed by Parliamentarian soldiers. Grantham's Eleanor Cross was located at the southern end of town, probably where the Tollemache Statue stands today. The cross at Stamford is believed to have stood at Scotgate, near the present-day Clock House, but all that has survived is one small marble fragment, a carved rose, which can be seen in the Stamford Museum. A modern sculpture inspired by the lost Eleanor Cross was erected in Stamford's Sheep Market in 2008.

34. In the 16th century the Old Hall was the home of Henry VIII's sixth wife, Katherine Parr, whilst she was married to her first husband, Edward de Burgh, second Baron Borough of Gainsborough.

35. In the 16th century Henry VIII dissolved the monasteries, a move that was highly unpopular with the ordinary people, and led to the 'Lincolnshire Rising'. It started in October 1536 in Louth, Horncastle and Caistor, from where people marched to Lincoln, gathering others from elsewhere in the county as they went. The worst incident was when Dr Raynes, Chancellor of Lincoln Cathedral, was dragged from Old Bolingbroke to Horncastle, and clubbed to death by the mob. The rebels were joined in Lincoln by a force from Boston, including some sympathetic members of the gentry, and sent a letter to the king listing their grievances. The king's reply was read out in the Chapter House of Lincoln Cathedral, in which he referred to the county of Lincolnshire as 'one of the most brute and beastly in the realm'. On the following day the gentry amongst the rebels decided to capitulate to the king's forces sent to Lincoln, and advised the ordinary people to go home, but Henry VIII was determined to make an example of Lincolnshire, and a number of rebels were hanged.

LINCOLN, THE CATHEDRAL FROM BRAYFORD c1950 L49051

36. The 11-mile-long Fossdyke Navigation from Brayford Pool in Lincoln to the River Trent at Torksey, which was built by the Romans more than 1,800 years ago and is still in use.

37. The Lucy Tower is Lincoln Castle's main keep, and is named after Countess Lucy de Taillebois who had it constructed in the twelfth century; she was Sheriff of Lincoln and Constable of the Castle until her death in 1136. In the winter of 1140 Lucy's sons Ranulf and William involved Lincoln in the civil war between King Stephen and his cousin Matilda, when they seized control of the castle. Lincoln's citizens appealed to the king, who came with an army to besiege the fortress; it is said he attacked the castle by placing bowmen and siege engines on the west front of the cathedral. A relieving rebel army arrived in February 1141 and joined battle with the king's army, which was supported by the loyal inhabitants of the city. The king's troops were overwhelmed, and despite fighting heroically with a Danish battle-axe given to him by a Lincoln citizen, Stephen was captured. The short battle became known as the 'Joust of Lincoln'. In the aftermath the city was sacked by the rebel army and many inhabitants were killed.

38. The word 'gate' in a street name is a corruption of a Norse word that means 'the way of' or 'the way to'. Thus Watergate means the way to the water, and Westgate means the way out of town to the west. The ancient Norse heritage of Lincolnshire from the time when it was under Danish control is evident in many of the county's place-names, especially those ending in '-by', '-toft', '-thorpe', and '-ness', meaning respectively 'town' or 'village', 'homestead', 'hamlet', and 'headland'.

39. After Lincoln Cathedral was partially destroyed by an earthquake in 1185, a plea was made for funds to help rebuild it, and a poor swineherd from Stow offered all his meagre savings to the project. Hearing of his generosity, Bishop Hugh of Lincoln (later canonised as St Hugh of Avalon) noted that he would be rewarded in heaven where all were equal. To represent this, a statue of Bishop Hugh was placed on the pinnacle of the right-hand corner tower of the west front, while on the left-hand tower 'The Swineherd of Stow' stands at exactly the same height.

BARTON UPON HUMBER, ST PETER'S CHURCH c1965 B750016

40. St Peter's Church at Barton-upon-Humber (photograph B750016, above) is one of England's best examples of an Anglo-Saxon church tower, and is a national as well as a Lincolnshire treasure (the rest of the church is 13th-century). The church was made redundant in 1972 and is now protected by English Heritage.

41. Now the headquarters of the Society for Lincolnshire History and Archaeology, the Jew's House on Steep Hill at Lincoln dates from the 1170s and is one of the oldest houses in England (see photograph 25664, opposite). It was owned by a Jewess, Belaset, in the 1280s. It was a merchant's house, with shops on the ground floor and the hall and chamber on the upper floor; the hall was heated by a stone fireplace above the doorway.

42. Red Lion Square was named after the long-closed Red Lion Inn, now the premises of the HSBC bank.

43. When first built in 1873, the pier at Cleethorpes was much longer than it is now, at 1,200 foot in length (see photograph 55741, page 13). During the Second World War it was feared that the pier presented an easy access point for sea-borne enemy invaders – they might be able to alight from ships or U-boats without entering inshore waters – so a middle section of the pier was removed, reducing the length of the part attached to land to just 355 feet. When the war ended, the Government was unable to fund a replacement middle section, so the isolated seaward section was demolished. Some of the salvaged material from the demolition of the seaward part of Cleethorpes Pier was used on Leicester City Football Club's new Filbert Street stand.

LINCOLN, THE JEW'S HOUSE 1890 25664

BOSTON, GUILDHALL 1893 32073

44. Almost all the land and farm holdings in Skegness belonged to the Earl of Scarbrough, and with the coming of the railway Lord Scarbrough decided to develop Skegness as a model watering place. Work began in 1877, and the next five years saw the tiny coastal village overlaid with wide tree-lined avenues, a new main street, promenades and villas, homes and lodging houses. Lumley Road and Lumley Square in Skegness were named after the Earl of Scarbrough's family name.

45. In the early 17th century some Protestants who followed an extreme form of worship, known as Puritans, felt that they were being persecuted and decided to leave the country to be free to worship in the way they wanted. A group from north Nottinghamshire, including William Brewster and William Bradford, tried to leave England in 1607, catching a boat from a creek downstream of Boston in an attempt to sail to the Netherlands. They were betrayed and captured, and put on trial in the court in Boston's Guildhall (photograph 32073, opposite); the cells that briefly held them can still be seen. The dissenters later sailed from Immingham to the Netherlands and in 1620 some of them, known as the Pilgrim Fathers, made their famous voyage to Massachusetts on the 'Mayflower' – including William Brewster and William Bradford, who had been previously detained in Boston.

46. Boston became famous as a centre of Puritanism in the first half of the 17th century, and many people from the area emigrated to the colony of Massachusetts in New England, in what is now the USA, in search of religious freedom – it is estimated that 250 of the 3,000 people then living in Boston emigrated to New England between 1629 and 1640. Men from Boston held one or other of the top jobs in the colony for the next 60 years, and the settlement of 'Boston' in Massachusetts was named after the Lincolnshire town from which these leaders came.

47. The North Sea was known as the German Ocean or German Sea until the early 20th century, when hostilities between Britain and Germany made the name unpopular.

48. Union Street and Union Place in Boston are so called because they were built about the same time as the Act of Union abolished the Irish Parliament and included Ireland in the United Kingdom.

49. In the days before tarmac the roads around Stamford were topped with limestone that made them dangerously slippery for cyclists, and cycle guides of the late 19th century wrote off this stretch of the Great North Road as being dangerously unrideable when wet.

50. The Lincoln Imp is a stone carving in the form of a small diabolical creature in Lincoln Cathedral. The builders of the shrine of St Hugh wanted pilgrims to have in mind the ever-present danger of evil, so they included a reminder of the devil high up between two arches on the north side of the Angel Choir (see photograph L49078, opposite).

51. The chief purpose of the Grimsby Dock Tower was to provide the massive head pressure of stored water necessary to operate the Royal Dock gates – these were necessary to harness the tidal ebb and flow of the Humber estuary. Latterly it provided a low-pressure water supply to the whole of Grimsby's extensive fish market. The pressure was supplied by a wrought iron tank capable of holding 30,000 gallons of water.

52. The famous 617 Squadron 'Dambusters' raid was organised from Grantham, and launched from RAF Scampton in 1943. The expression 'Bomber County' was an apt description for Lincolnshire during the Second World War – at that time there were 46 aerodromes in the county, more than in any other.

LINCOLN
THE LINCOLN IMP
c1955 L49078

TRADE AND INDUSTRY

53. This means that the tower was paid for from the profits made by the merchants importing and exporting wool through the medieval port of Boston. In the Middle Ages Boston Fair was one of the main places in England where wool was bought and sold.

54. Legend says that Robin Hood and his Merry Men dressed in 'Lincoln green' cloth to camouflage themselves in Sherwood Forest.

55. The Hornsby company, a pioneer in the development of heavy oil engines; the first mass-produced diesel engines were built in its factory from 1891. Hornsby's amalgamated in 1918 with Ruston, Proctor & Co of Lincoln to become Ruston & Hornsby, renowned for the diesel engines it produced for both land and marine applications. Ruston & Hornsby also built diesel locomotives from 1931 to 1967, and developed gas turbines from the 1950s. The Grantham factory of Ruston & Hornsby closed in 1963.

56. Geese, valued for their meat, feathers and quills. Geese were bred on the Lincolnshire fens in great numbers and their feathers were plucked twice a year to fill feather beds and pillows. In the 19th and 20th centuries, Boston was the centre of the fenland feather industry, with several factories purifying feathers for pillows and other purposes. Now the only business left in this industry is Fogarty's, which also uses man-made fillers.

57. Clayton & Shuttleworth made highly efficient portable steam engines, which had a number of purposes, including the driving of farm machinery, and the company became the largest manufacturer of steam engines and threshing machines in Britain.

58. Tanks are so called because the workmen who built the hulls of the first vehicles during the First World War were told that they were building tracked water containers or 'water tanks' for the army, in order for the production of these new fighting vehicles to be kept secret.

GENERAL KNOWLEDGE - LINCOLNSHIRE

59. A 'Yellowbelly'. There are many theories about the origin of the name, one being that it derives from the bright yellow waistcoat worn by the 10th Regiment of Foot, later The Lincolnshire Regiment.

60. Boston's town centre is dominated by the mighty tower of St Botolph's Church, universally known as the Boston Stump (seen in the background of photograph 26067, below). Crowned by a superb octagonal lantern complete with pinnacles and flying buttresses, it soars 272 feet above the town and can be seen from miles around; it used to serve as a landmark for shipping, for the lantern once used to have a beacon lit in it at night. The church, dedicated to the Saxon monk St Botolph, gave its name to the town, which was called 'St Botolph's' or 'Botolph's Town' until about 1400, after which date the shorter name of 'Boston' has been used.

BOSTON, A RIVER VIEW 1890 26067

61. The dual-carriageway known as John Adams Way in Boston is named after the second president of the USA, John Adams, who was a lawyer in Boston, Massachusetts at the time of the American Revolution and a champion of liberty. His connection with Boston in Lincolnshire is that his wife's ancestors (named Quincy) came from this area. His eldest son, John Quincy Adams, became the sixth president of the USA in 1825.

62. Lincolnshire sausages are a distinctive variety of pork sausage that has a dominant flavour of herbs, with sage being the traditional flavouring. They are also notable for having an open, chunky texture, being made with pork that is coarsely ground, rather than minced.

63. A wild plant which is sometimes called 'poor man's asparagus' is Marsh Samphire, or glasswort, a delicacy found growing in salt marshes around the coast of Lincolnshire. The green fleshy tips of this succulent, bright green plant can be eaten either raw or lightly cooked. Samphire is in season from about the end of July, and should be collected by cutting it with scissors, not pulling up by the roots, so that it can grow again the next year.

64. Stamford.

65. In February 2008, Scunthorpe and the surrounding area in north Lincolnshire was shaken by one of the most powerful earthquakes ever recorded in Britain; it lasted for 10 seconds, and measured 5.2 on the Richter scale.

66. The statue on the roof of the former Stamford Hotel, now the Stamford Walk shopping mall, is by J C F Rossi, R A, and represents the figure of Justice.

67. 'The Jolly Fisherman', popularly known as 'Jolly'. He was designed in 1908 by John Hassell for use on a poster for the Great Northern Railway advertising the attractions of Skegness, accompanied by the equally famous slogan 'Skegness is so bracing', which has become one of the most famous advertisements ever made.

67. The south porch of St Wulfram's Church in Grantham contains one of the town's great treasures, the chained library. It was founded in 1598 by the Rev Francis Trigge, rector of the nearby village of Welbourn. The library contains a total of 82 chained books. The earliest is dated 1472, and is bound with two others dated 1476. In a chained library the books are attached to their bookcase by a chain which is just long enough to allow the books to be taken from their shelves and read, but not to be removed or stolen from the library itself.

69. The International Kite Flying Festival.

70. Grant's the butchers' shop which formerly stood in Stamford's High Street was dismantled in 1936 and moved to the York Castle Museum, where it was reconstructed to form part of the museum's famous Victorian street scene, 'Kirkgate'. It can be seen in photograph 72302 (below) when it was still trading in Stamford – it is the gabled building, second from the left.

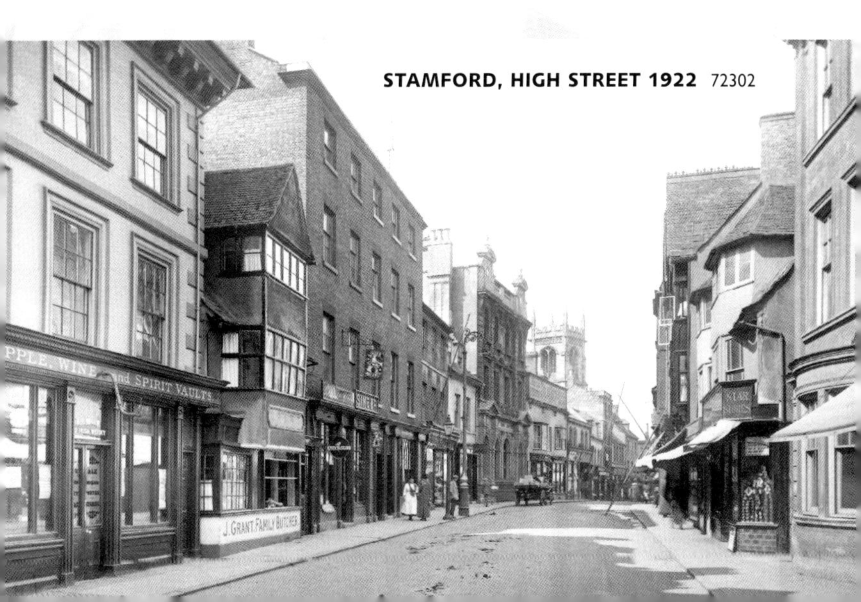

STAMFORD, HIGH STREET 1922 72302

GRANTHAM ST WULFRAN'S CHURCH 1890
27846

71. St Wulfram's Church in Grantham (photograph 27846, left). Simon Jenkins said of it: 'Here is the finest steeple in England. When seen from the railway or across the flatlands of west Lincolnshire, Grantham's slender spike is one of the exhilarating images of English Gothic'. The west front of the church, which includes the tower and spire, was started around 1280. It was the first spire of the period to reach such a great height – it is nearly 283 feet high.

72. At Sandilands, just south of Sutton-on-Sea. St Clement's parish church in Sandilands is Lincolnshire's very own Leaning Tower, doubtless owing to its sandy foundations having settled since it was built in 1819 (see photograph S480042, below).

SANDILANDS, THE CROOKED CHURCH c1955
S480042

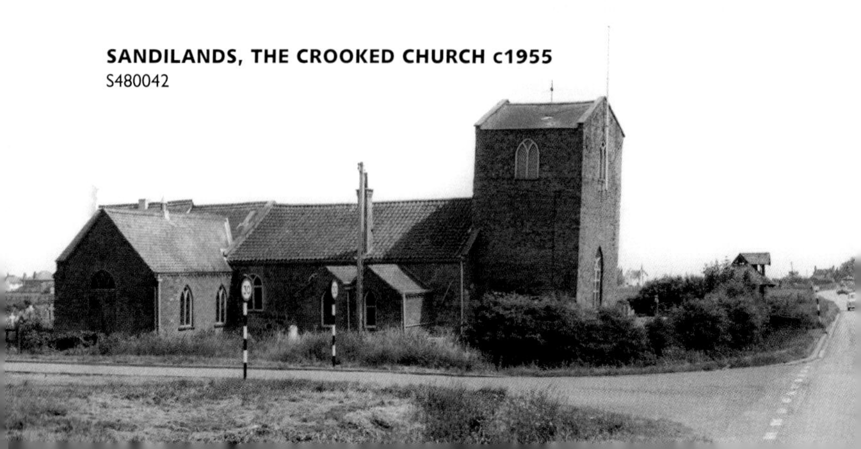

73. Louth is famous for its superb and grand church, crowned by its 295ft-high spire, built in the early 1500s (see photograph L305016, page 30).

74. Edith Smith Way in Grantham is named after Edith Smith, Britain's first 'official' full-time woman police constable with powers of arrest. Edith joined the police force in 1915, during the First World War, when thousands of soldiers were billeted in the area. It was her job to keep an eye on the many ladies of dubious virtue who were attracted to Grantham because of all these troops, and make sure that they didn't cause trouble. Apparently she was kept so busy 'keeping an eye on frivolous girls likely to get into mischief' that she worked seven days a week for two years, without ever having a day off!

75. The church at Great Ponton near Grantham bears an unusual weather-vane in the shape of a violin. The present version is a replica of the original which was placed there in the 17th century, paid for as a 'thank you' by a grateful fiddler who emigrated to America and made his fortune there after local villagers raised the money for his fare.

76. Lincoln was first established as a Roman legionary fortress and later became a Roman walled town, a 'colonia', or settlement for retired Roman legionaries. The area's earlier name, of Celtic-British origin, was 'Lindum', meaning 'a settlement by a pool, or lake', and so the Roman town was known as 'Lindum Colonia'. In Anglo-Saxon times that name changed from 'Lindocolonia' to 'Lyndcylene', and then to Lincoln.

GRANTHAM, THE BEE HIVE INN c1955 G43051

77. The George Hotel at Stamford is noted for its 'gallows' sign spanning the road, which is thought to be an attempt at curing instability in the front wall arising from when it was rebuilt in 1724.

78. Perched in a tree outside the Beehive Inn at Grantham is the 'living sign' of a real beehive, which is still there, complete with a resident colony of honey bees (see photograph G43051, above). The pub itself is of great antiquity, and there has been a beehive in a tree there since the early 1700s, although not the same one.

79. By 2003, Grimsby was officially Britain's luckiest lottery town, with eleven major wins in the area since the first draw in 1994. Individual wins of £14 million, £8 million and £3 million alone have helped earn Grimsby the nickname of 'Winsby', and experts have theorised that Grimsby's population is two-and-a-half times more likely to land a fortune than that of the rest of Britain.

FAMOUS PEOPLE

80. Sir Isaac Newton. As a boy, he attended what is now the Old School (then a grammar school) in Grantham in the early 1600s – the building is now used as a library by King's School. Young Isaac Newton carved his name on one of its windowsills, which can still be seen. In later life, it was at his home of Woolsthorpe Manor near Grantham that he is said to have watched an apple fall to the ground and begun to understand the law of gravity. An imposing statue of Sir Isaac Newton stands on what is now known as St Peter's Hill in Grantham, which was erected in 1857 (see photograph 22286, below).

GRANTHAM, THE GUILDHALL 1889 22286

81. The Bass Strait, between Tasmania and south Australia, which is named after George Bass of Boston, a Royal Naval surgeon and explorer. Another Lincolnshire man involved in the exploration of Australia was Matthew Flinders of Donington, who named many places on the Eyre Peninsula of south Australia from Lincolnshire, such as Port Lincoln, Boston Island, Revesby Cove, and Cape Donington.

82. Sir John Franklin's last expedition was to find the North-West Passage around the north of Canada, but Franklin and his crews died in 1847 when his ships, 'Erebus' and 'Terror', were trapped in the Arctic ice.

83. Hereward the Wake ('the watchful'). The Anglo-Saxon freedom fighter against the Normans of the 11th century came from a landowning family in Bourne in Lincolnshire. After the Norman invasion, Hereward's brother was killed at Bourne whilst protecting his family and estate, causing Hereward to take up arms in revenge. In 1069 he was party to the sacking of the Anglo-Saxon monastery at Peterborough, using the appointment of an unpopular Norman abbot as the excuse for doing this. Afterwards he took refuge in the Isle of Ely, where he held out for around three years. The Normans broke into Ely eventually, but Hereward managed to escape. What happened to him later is not known, but legend says that after his death he was buried in the abbey grounds at Crowland, in Lincolnshire.

84. Daniel Lambert was the heaviest man in Britain at the time of his death, aged 39, in 1809. He weighed in at almost 53 stone. He died at the Waggon and Horses Inn whilst on a visit to Stamford races, and part of the inn had to be demolished to allow his coffin to be removed. A painting of Daniel Lambert can be seen in the foyer of the George Hotel, in Stamford, and the Stamford Museum in Broad Street has some of his clothing on display.

GRIMSBY, THE ROYAL DOCK c1955 G60019

85. George Boole was born in Silver Street in Lincoln in 1815, the son of a shoemaker. He spent his twenties working as a schoolmaster and lecturer in the city. He was the author of Boolean Logic and a pioneer of binary notation, and hence one of the pioneers of the modern computer age.

86. Grantham was the birthplace in 1925 of Margaret Thatcher, Britain's first female Prime Minister – she was also the first woman to lead a major Western democracy. Her father, Alfred Roberts, an Alderman and Methodist lay preacher, had two grocery shops in the town; Margaret was brought up in a flat over the largest shop, in North Parade, and attended Grantham Girls' School.

FRANCIS FRITH

PIONEER VICTORIAN PHOTOGRAPHER

Francis Frith, founder of the world-famous photographic archive, was a complex and multi-talented man. A devout Quaker and a highly successful Victorian businessman, he was philosophical by nature and pioneering in outlook. By 1855 he had already established a wholesale grocery business in Liverpool, and sold it for the astonishing sum of £200,000, which is the equivalent today of over £15,000,000. Now in his thirties, and captivated by the new science of photography, Frith set out on a series of pioneering journeys up the Nile and to the Near East.

INTRIGUE AND EXPLORATION

He was the first photographer to venture beyond the sixth cataract of the Nile. Africa was still the mysterious 'Dark Continent', and Stanley and Livingstone's historic meeting was a decade into the future. The conditions for picture taking confound belief. He laboured for hours in his wicker dark-room in the sweltering heat of the desert, while the volatile chemicals fizzed dangerously in their trays. Back in London he exhibited his photographs and was 'rapturously cheered' by members of the Royal Society. His reputation as a photographer was made overnight.

VENTURE OF A LIFE-TIME

By the 1870s the railways had threaded their way across the country, and Bank Holidays and half-day Saturdays had been made obligatory by Act of Parliament. All of a sudden the working man and his family were able to enjoy days out, take holidays, and see a little more of the world.

With typical business acumen, Francis Frith foresaw that these new tourists would enjoy having souvenirs to commemorate their days out. For the next thirty years he travelled the country by train and by pony and trap, producing fine photographs of seaside resorts and beauty spots that were keenly bought by millions of Victorians. These prints were painstakingly pasted into family albums and pored over during the dark nights of winter, rekindling precious memories of summer excursions. Frith's studio was soon supplying retail shops all over the country, and by 1890 F Frith & Co had become the greatest specialist photographic publishing company in the world, with over 2,000 sales outlets, and pioneered the picture postcard.

FRANCIS FRITH'S LEGACY

Francis Frith had died in 1898 at his villa in Cannes, his great project still growing. By 1970 the archive he created contained over a third of a million pictures showing 7,000 British towns and villages.

Frith's legacy to us today is of immense significance and value, for the magnificent archive of evocative photographs he created provides a unique record of change in the cities, towns and villages throughout Britain over a century and more. Frith and his fellow studio photographers revisited locations many times down the years to update their views, compiling for us an enthralling and colourful pageant of British life and character.

We are fortunate that Frith was dedicated to recording the minutiae of everyday life. For it is this sheer wealth of visual data, the painstaking chronicle of changes in dress, transport, street layouts, buildings, housing and landscape that captivates us so much today, offering us a powerful link with the past and with the lives of our ancestors.

Computers have now made it possible for Frith's many thousands of images to be accessed almost instantly. The archive offers every one of us an opportunity to examine the places where we and our families have lived and worked down the years. Its images, depicting our shared past, are now bringing pleasure and enlightenment to millions around the world a century and more after his death.

For further information visit: www.francisfrith.com

INTERIOR DECORATION

Frith's photographs can be seen framed and as giant wall murals in thousands of pubs, restaurants, hotels, banks, retail stores and other public buildings throughout Britain. These provide interesting and attractive décor, generating strong local interest and acting as a powerful reminder of gentler days in our increasingly busy and frenetic world.

FRITH PRODUCTS

All Frith photographs are available as prints and posters in a variety of different sizes and styles. In the UK we also offer a range of other gift and stationery products illustrated with Frith photographs, although many of these are not available for delivery outside the UK – see our web site for more information on the products available for delivery in your country.

THE INTERNET

Over 100,000 photographs of Britain can be viewed and purchased on the Frith web site. The web site also includes memories and reminiscences contributed by our customers, who have personal knowledge of localities and of the people and properties depicted in Frith photographs. If you wish to learn more about a specific town or village you may find these reminiscences fascinating to browse. Why not add your own comments if you think they would be of interest to others? See **www.francisfrith.com**

PLEASE HELP US BRING FRITH'S PHOTOGRAPHS TO LIFE

Our authors do their best to recount the history of the places they write about. They give insights into how particular towns and villages developed, they describe the architecture of streets and buildings, and they discuss the lives of famous people who lived there. But however knowledgeable our authors are, the story they tell is necessarily incomplete.

Frith's photographs are so much more than plain historical documents. They are living proofs of the flow of human life down the generations. They show real people at real moments in history; and each of those people is the son or daughter of someone, the brother or sister, aunt or uncle, grandfather or grandmother of someone else. All of them lived, worked and played in the streets depicted in Frith's photographs.

We would be grateful if you would give us your insights into the places shown in our photographs: the streets and buildings, the shops, businesses and industries. Post your memories of life in those streets on the Frith website: what it was like growing up there, who ran the local shop and what shopping was like years ago; if your workplace is shown tell us about your working day and what the building is used for now. Read other visitors' memories and reconnect with your shared local history and heritage. With your help more and more Frith photographs can be brought to life, and vital memories preserved for posterity, and for the benefit of historians in the future.

Wherever possible, we will try to include some of your comments in future editions of our books. Moreover, if you spot errors in dates, titles or other facts, please let us know, because our archive records are not always completely accurate—they rely on 140 years of human endeavour and hand-compiled records. You can email us using the contact form on the website.

Thank you!

For further information, trade, or author enquiries
please contact us at the address below:

The Francis Frith Collection, Frith's Barn, Teffont, Salisbury, Wiltshire, England SP3 5QP.

Tel: +44 (0)1722 716 376 Fax: +44 (0)1722 716 881
e-mail: sales@francisfrith.co.uk **www.francisfrith.com**